BEDŘICH SMETANA

THE BARTERED BRIDE

A Comic Opera in Three Acts

The Libretto by

KAREL SABINA

English Translation by

LIBUSHKA BARTUSEK

Vocal Score & Optional Dialogue $4.00
Chorus Parts .... .40

Stage Guide and Orchestration available on rental from the publishers.

REMICK MUSIC CORPORATION
New York

(G)

CONTENTS

CAST OF CHARACTERS

Krushina (Kroo'-shi-na) a peasant .... Baritone
Ludmila (Lood'-mi-la) his wife .... Soprano
Marie, their daughter .... Soprano
Micha (Mee'-ha) a landowner .... Bass
Hata (Hah'-tah) his wife .... Mezzo-soprano
Vashek (Vah'-shek) their son .... Tenor
Jenik (Yeh'-nyeek) Micha's son by a former marriage .... Tenor
Kezal (Keht'-zal) the village marriage broker .... Bass
Principal Comedian, head of troupe of strolling actors .... Tenor
Esmeralda, a member of the troupe .... Soprano
Indian, another member of the troupe .... Tenor

Villagers, troupers, children

SCENE

A village in Bohemia, Feast-day. Action taking place from noon, immediately after church service, until twilight. About 1850.

THE STORY

It is Feast-day in a Bohemian village . . . the day that Kezal, the marriage-broker, has chosen for the meeting of the Krushina and Micha families. The object of this meeting is to arrange a marriage between Marie, the daughter of the peasant Krushina, and Vashek, the son of Micha the wealthy landowner. Marie, however, loves Jenik, a youth but recently employed in the village. He returns her love. but feels that he must not disclose his identity.

Kezal, knowing that Micha will pay him handsomely for the transaction, is forcing the match favoring the simple Vashek. He approaches Jenik with the offer of another bride and three hundred gold pieces. Jenik accepts the proffered sum, but only on condition that Marie will be given in marriage to no other excepting Micha's son. The marriage-broker readily agrees to the terms proposed and the contract is signed.

Marie, heartbroken at her lover's perfidy, is finally prevailed upon to consent to wed Vashek . . . the parents and villagers are summoned to witness the bethrothal . . . when Jenik steps forth and Micha recognizes in him the son who left home because of his quarrelsome step-mother.

As Micha's son, Jenik claims his right to the hand of the lovely Marie. Hata, the step-mother insists that the original plan be followed, but when Vashek appears in the guise of a bear (he had been substituting for a tippling member of a troupe of strolling players) Kezal himself realizes his failure at match-making and Micha bestows his blessings upon Marie and Jenik.

BEDŘICH SMETANA
(1824 - 1884)

A genius, whether political, literary or artistic granted in a period of dire need—a moment of darkness—is the noblest gift the gods can bestow upon a people . . . Such a gift to Bohemia was Bedrich Smetana, the founder of modern Czech music, the man who dared create an art in the Czech idiom, when such expression was close kin to treason.

Like Mozart with whom he is so often compared, Smetana showed great promise in his early childhood, for at the tender age of five he was composing and concertizing . . . Later he studied with Proksh and Liszt . . . At the age of twenty-four he married Katerina Kolàr, but his happiness with her and their gifted little daughter was short-lived; within ten years he was cruelly bereft of both . . . The strain of political inharmony was somewhat alleviated by his appointment to the conductor's stand of the Gothenberg (Sweden) Philharmonic Society (1856) . . . Ten years later he became conductor of the Czech National Theatre in Prague . . . But, once again fate dealt a tragic blow, when Smetana's increasing deafness compelled him to leave this post.

Smetana's ardent nationalism is felt in all his compositions; it is most strongly emphasized, perhaps, in the best known of his eight operas "The Bartered Bride." However, the idea that Czech folktunes are the back-bone of the above-mentioned work is erroneous. With the exception of the second act "Furiant." there is no transcription of folk-melodies thruout the score, though characteristic rhythms are frequently employed . . . Still, every phrase of this masterpiece is an inspired pulsation of a Czech-imbued soul asserting its nationalism.

L. B.

The Bartered Bride

Overture

BEDŘICH SMETANA

G

9

Act I

Scene: Village square, Inn at side. Feast day.

Scene I

Marie, Jenik and Villagers

tem-pers, ir-ri-ta-tions, ir-ri-ta-tions, Heigh - - - ho!

tem-pers, ir-ri - ta-tions, ir-ri - ta-tions, Heigh - - - ho!

Why not sing of joy and glad-ness, why not ban-ish cares and sad-ness, when we're blest with

rug-ged health, hap-pi-ness, when we're blest with rug-ged health, hap-pi-ness, when we're blest with per-fect health. __

(14) **Piu mosso.**

He a - lone knows true con - tent - ment, who en - joys life to its full, to its full, He a - lone knows

(14) **Più mosso.**

Tutti

true con - tent - ment, who en - joys life to its full, to its full, who en - joys life to its full, to its full,

who en - joys life to its full! ——

(16) **Meno vivo.** p Jenik

Why are you so mel - an - cho - ly, my dear Ma - rie? ——

Clar.

Ob.

(16) pp dolce elegico

smorz.

don't de - lay, the mu - sic starts to play. don't de - lay, don't de - lay!

sempre al *p* *dim.*

don't de - lay, don't de - lay, don't de - lay, don't de - lay, don't de - lay!

piu pp (Exeunt)

Scene II

Marie and Jenik

Rec. (or Dialogue ∗)

Marie

So af - ter all, it real - ly is to be!

Jenik

Ah, what sad - ness mine! Dear - est one! Tell me what clouds your sweet face? What has

Strgs. *sfz*

Marie

hap - pened? Do not be sur - prised, dear, Mi - cha comes here to - day to ar - range all for his son's suit for my

Aria
Moderato. ♩=80

Marie

Con anima.

Were I e'er to learn that you had tru-ly ceased to care for me. to learn that you had for-sak-en me, all the ha-tred and re-venge I would in-voke and wreak on thee, re-venge would I wreak on thee, all the ha-tred and re-venge I would in-voke and wreak on thee, all___ re-venge I'd wreak on thee, all___ re-venge I'd wreak on thee.

There-fore tell me. my___ be-lov-ed, why your

thee.   There-fore tell me, my___ be-

lov - èd.   why your ang - er knows no bounds,   why you left your home___ and kin - dred and your

ire to me re - dounds, Ah!___   Your ire to me re - dounds, your ire - - - - now to

me___ re - dounds?   Tell me my be - lov - ed.

Tell me my be - lov - ed.

Recitative (or Dialogue *)

Duet

Scene III

Ludmila, Krushina and Kezal

Kez. shrewd and wise, so that to my ea - gle eyes that, to my sharp eyes no ti - ny thing is ev - er lost, no

Kez. ti - ny thing is ev - er lost, no ti - ny thing has ev - er missed my eyes.

Kez. And if your un - ru - ly daugh-ter dare re - sist with fool - ing, you'll wit - ness,

Kez. I'm pre-pared to give her the prop - er school-ing, pro-per school-ing, pro-per school - ing! Tutti

Kez. As I tell you, my dear neigh-bor and, as I tell you, you gave your word of hon-or, and as soon as it was

Kez. spok-en, all plans were set and done. So all is set and done, so all is set and done, is set and

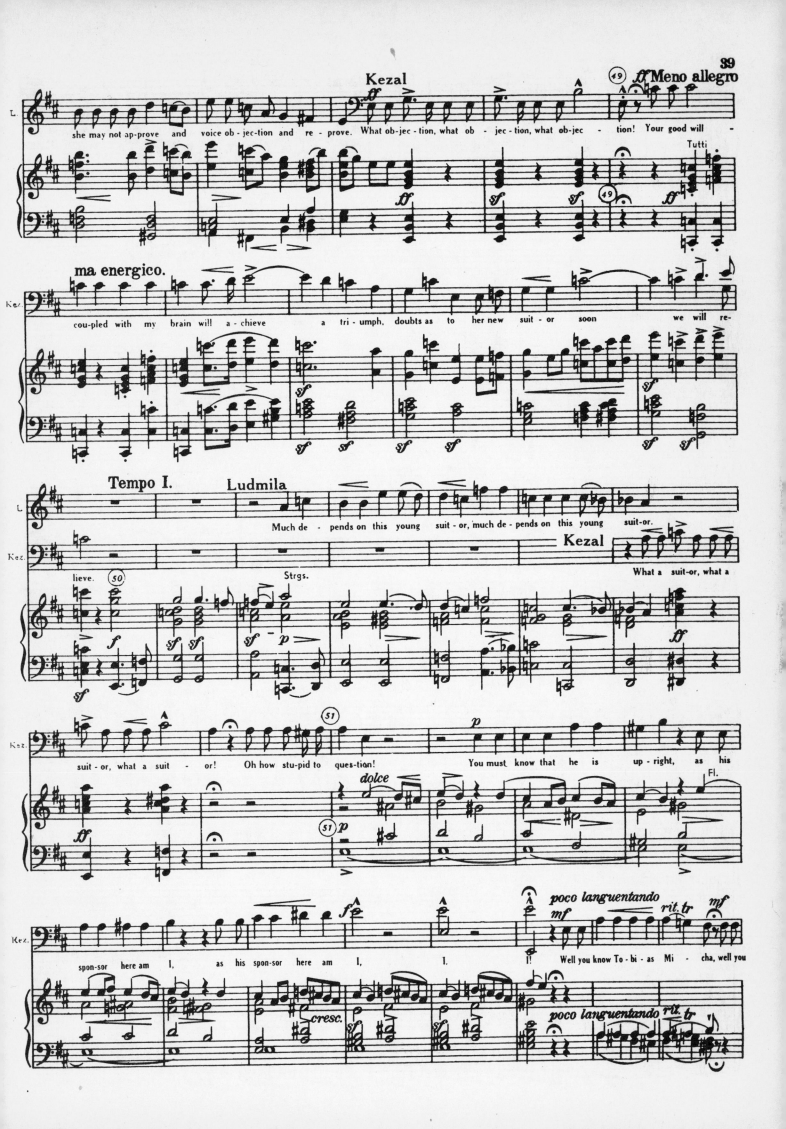

Recitative (or Dialogue *)

Trio
Andante, ma non troppo. ♩ = 60

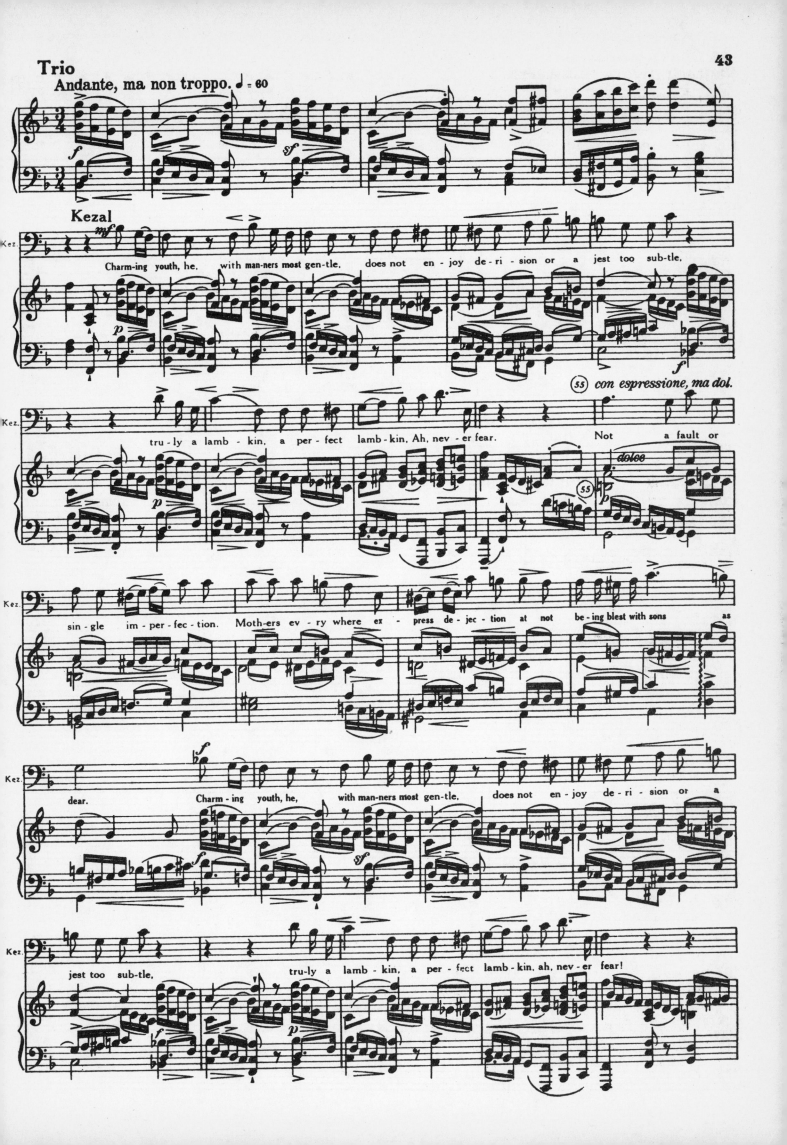

Kezal

Charm-ing youth, he, with man-ners most gen-tle, does not en - joy de - ri - sion or a jest too sub-tle.

tru - ly a lamb - kin, a per - fect lamb-kin, Ah, nev - er fear. Not a fault or

single im - per - fec - tion. Moth-ers ev - ry where ex - press de - jec - tion at not be - ing blest with sons as

dear. Charm - ing youth, he, with man-ners most gen-tle, does not en - joy de - ri - sion or a

jest too sub-tle, tru - ly a lamb - kin, a per - fect lamb - kin, ah, nev - er fear!

Scene IV
Marie, Ludmila, Krushina and Kezal

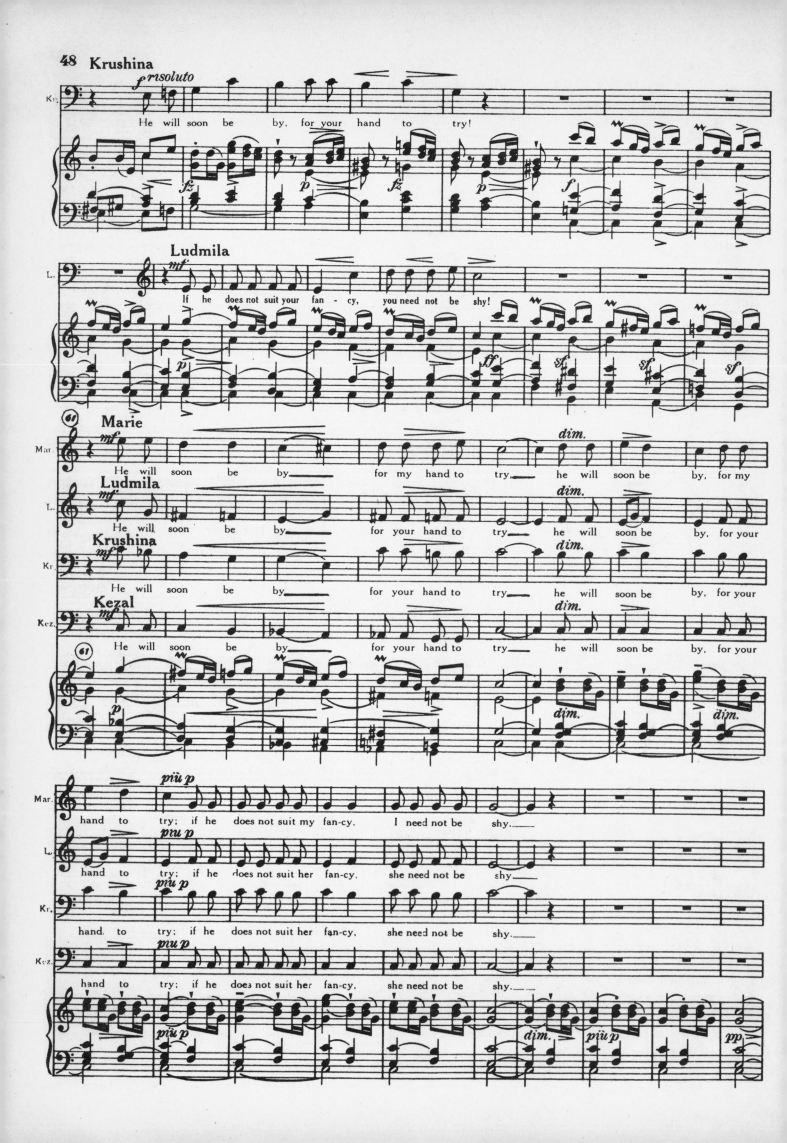

Tempo I. vivo.

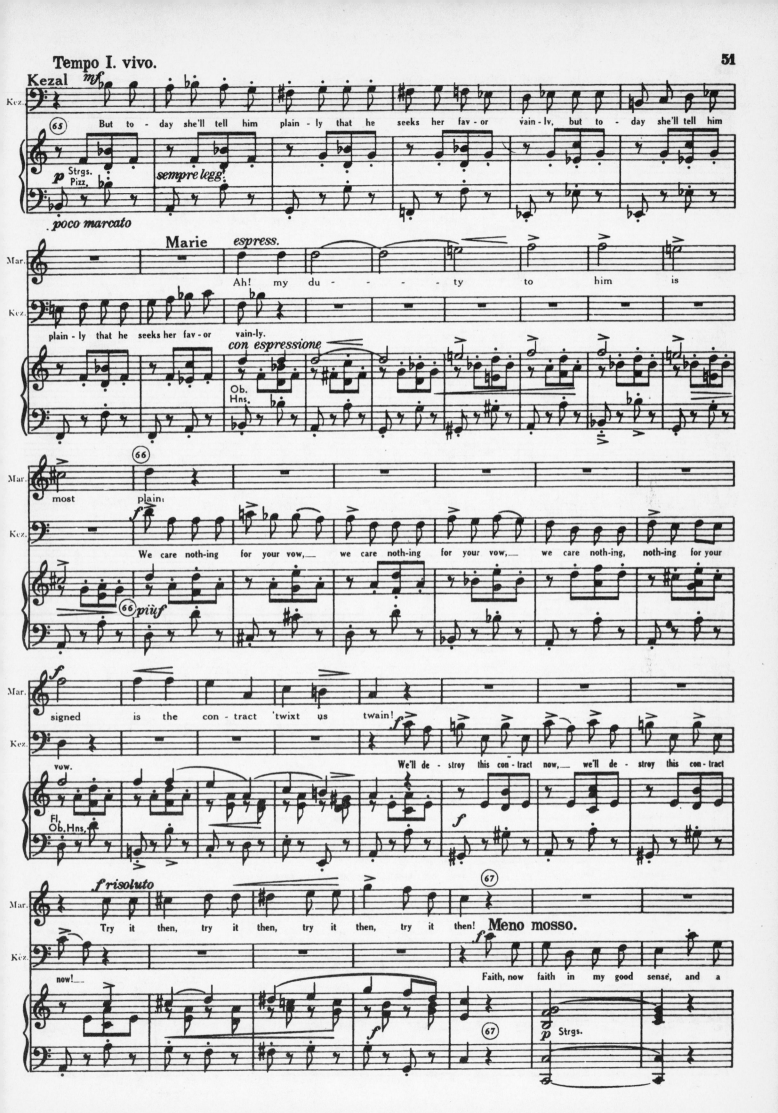

Recitative (or Dialogue *)

Scene V
Finale

Enter Villagers. Elders seat themselves at tables, youths prepare to dance.

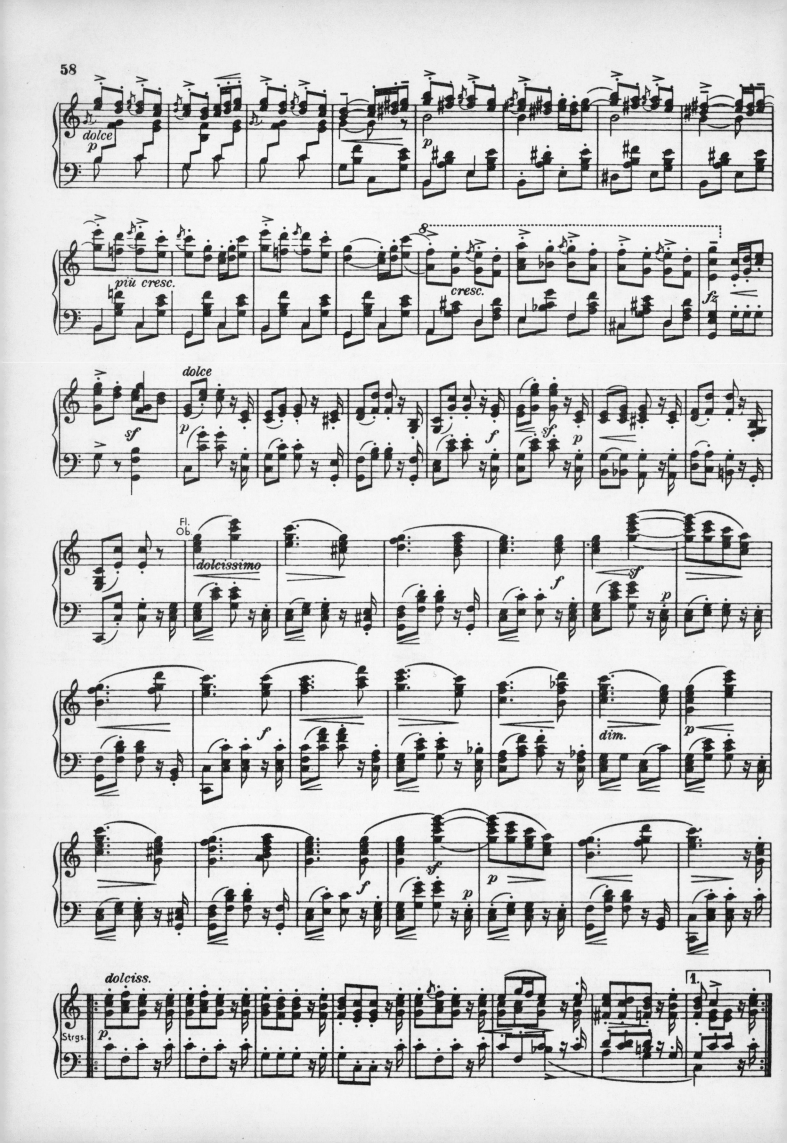

This is a traditional cut
not included in orchestration

Basses

Join my sway-ing, turn-ing, sway-ing, while the hap-py pol-ka's play - ing, join my sway-ing,

Tenors

marcato il basso

turn - ing, sway - ing, while the hap-py pol-ka's play - ing.

Tenors
Basses

sempre f

Join my sway-ing, turn-ing, sway-ing, while the hap-py

sempre f

marcato sempre

pol-ka's play - ing, hand in hand and face to face, gai - ly whirl-ing thru-out space!

End of Act I

Act II

Scene I

Scene: Interior of Inn. Jenik and Village youths at one side,
at tables, drinking; Kezal at the opposite side.

FURIANT.

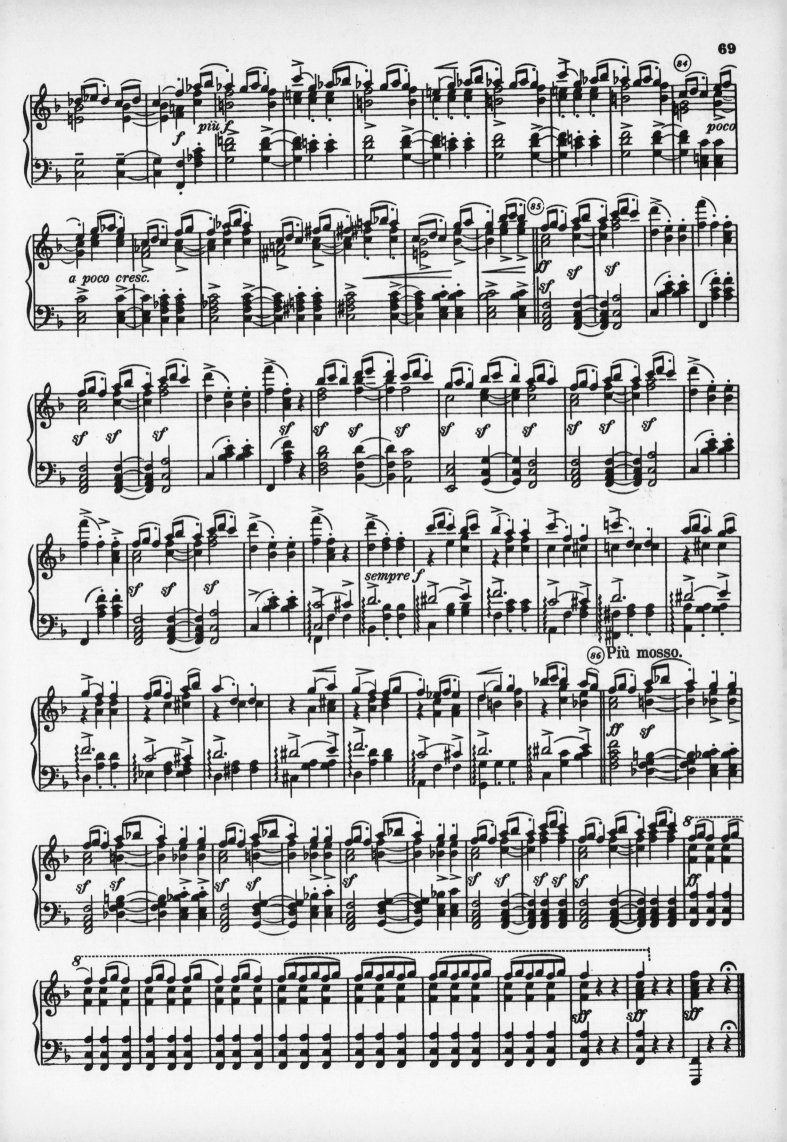

Scene II

Scene III
Marie, Vashek

Recitative (or Dialogue *)

Scene IV.

Jenik and Kezal

Recitative (or Dialogue *)

Kezal: I tell you, she's pret-ty, and good, wealth-y too, and bears the name of Bie-la!

Jenik: But then, who can tell that I would be her choice!

Kezal: That is my af-fair, just tell me that you tru-ly re-nounce Ma-rie!

Jenik: No, I can-not! Would you that I die of heart-break!

Kezal: Fools there were who car-ried weap-ons!

Moderato.

Mon-ey al-ways is an as-set!

Jenik: Well, and this one whom you have found for me, is she thus fa-vored?

Kezal: Sure-ly!

Duet
Allegro commodo. ♩=92

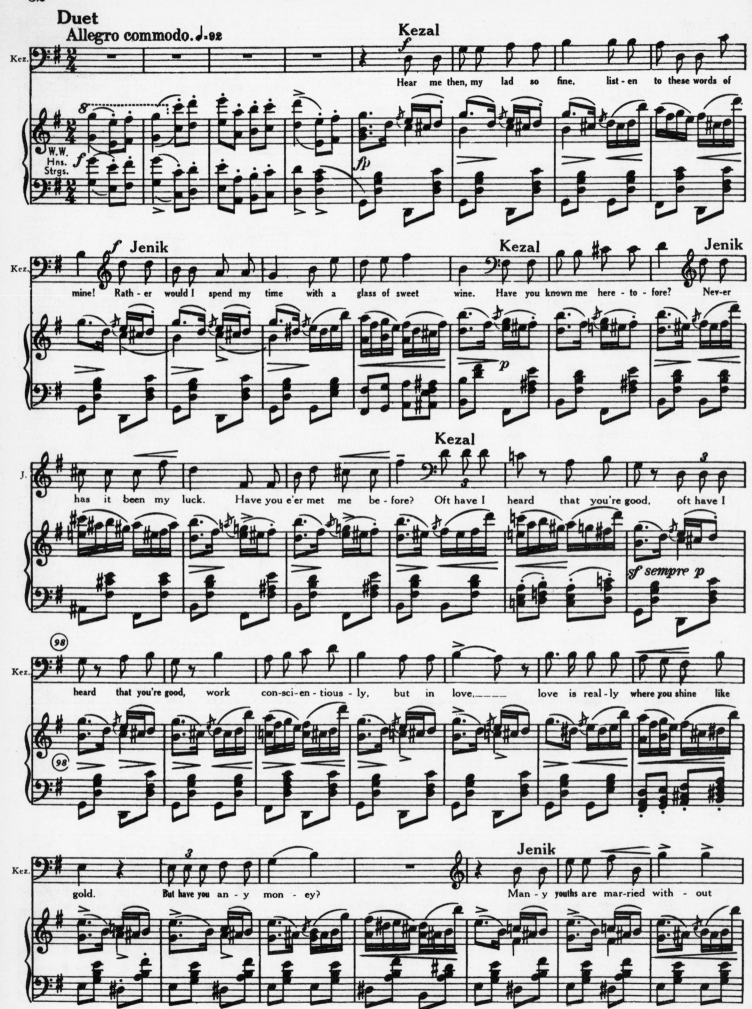

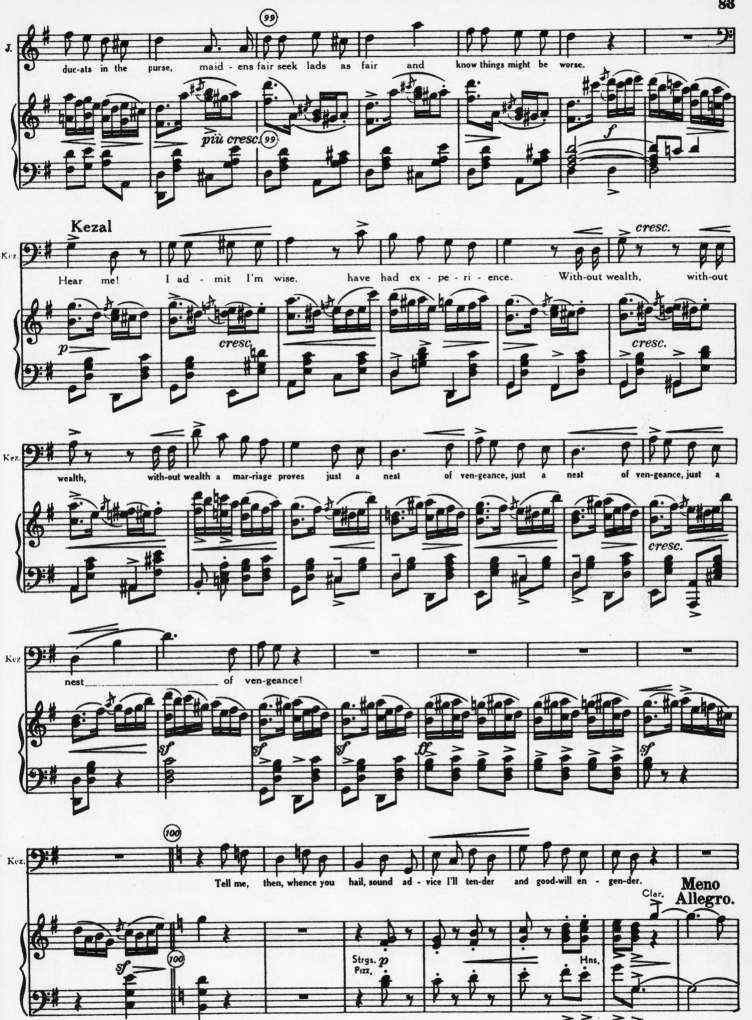

Tempo I.

Recitative (or Dialogue ✳)

Scene V

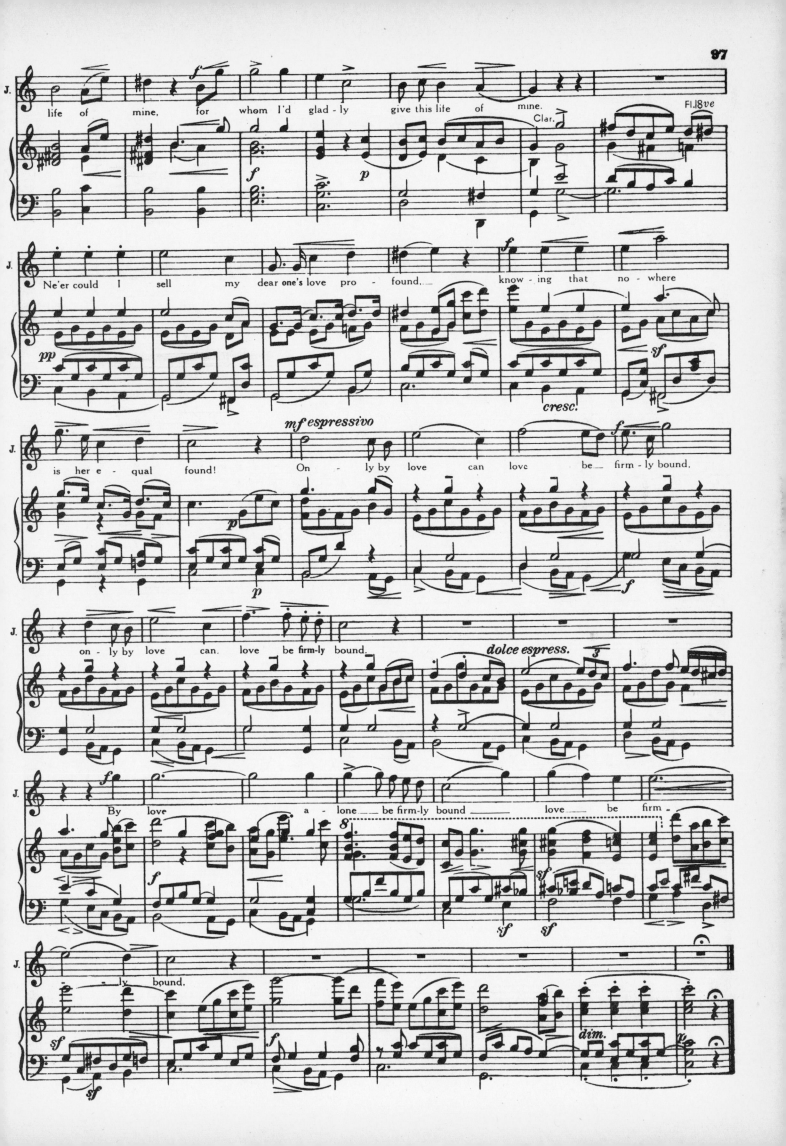

Scene VI

Jenik, Kezal, Krushina, Villagers

(Curtain)

End of Act II

Act III

Scene: Village square, Inn at side.

Scene I
Vashek

Scene II
March of the Strolling Players

Recitative (Dialogue optional *)

Principal

I an-nounce to my il - lus - tri-ous pub-lic, that here to - day, in-as-much as it is feast-day, there will be a per-form-ance

of a nat-ure most note - wor-thy, hith-er-to un-seen com-e-dy on the tight-rope, horse-back, al-so on the ground!

Add to this, grace-ful Miss Es-me-ral-da Sa-la-man-ka, who will, for your pleas-ure,

Allegro moderato.

Pr. Hop-ing that our dear pub-lic will then hon-or us to-night, we in-vite you all in deep-est es-

teem! How-ev-er, just a small re-hear-sal for your be-ne-fit, at once. Ho-la, get start-ed!

GALOP
Ballet and Act of Players

Vivace. ♩. = 144

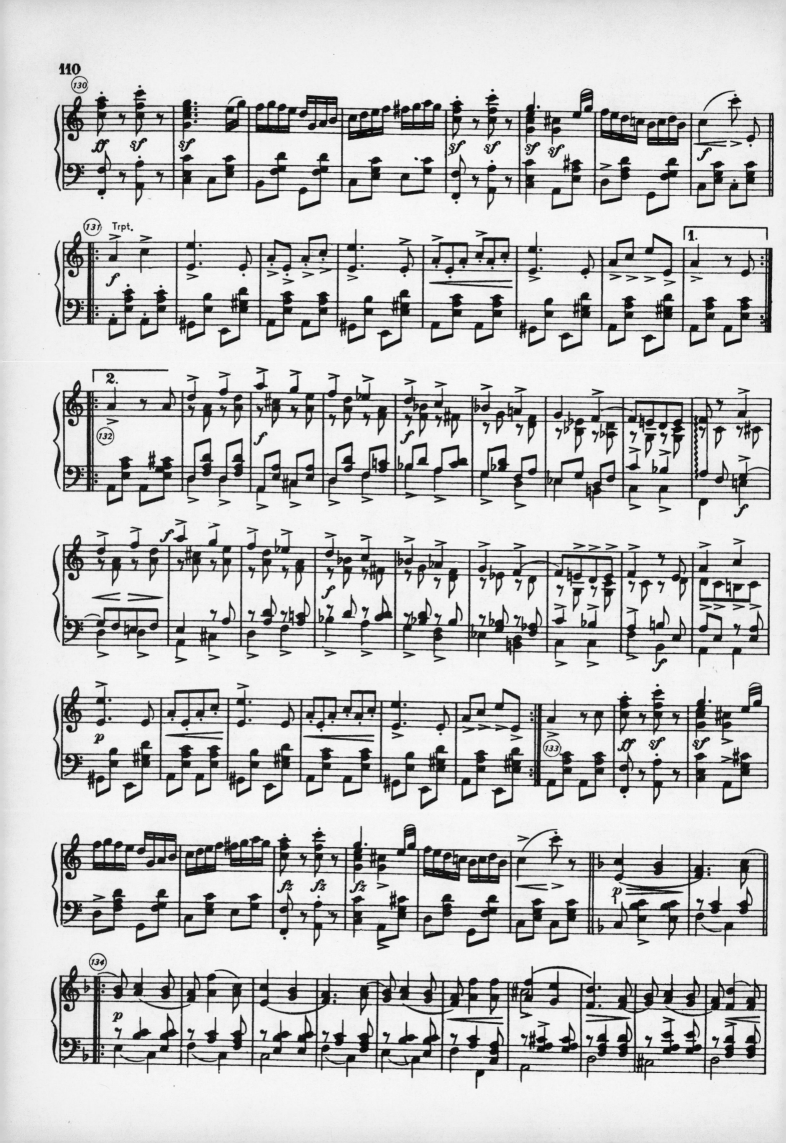

Scene III

Recitative (Dialogue optional *)

Scene IV

Hata, Kezal, Micha, Vashek

144 Più mosso.
Hata
Ha.
Sounds like an im-po-si-tion. Sounds like an im-po-si-tion, no one,
Micha
Mi.
Sounds like an im-po-si-tion. Sounds like an im-po-si-tion. no one,
Kezal
Kez.
Sounds like an im-po-si-tion. Sounds like an im-po-si-tion, no one,
144 Più mosso.
pp
cresc.
molto cresc.
f
no oth-er would de-vise it, ex-cept that boor him-self, no one, no oth-er would de-vise it, ex-
no oth-er would de-vise it, ex-cept that boor him-self, no one, no oth-er would de-vise it, ex-
no oth-er would de-vise it, ex-cept that boor him-self, no one, no oth-er would de-vise it, ex-
sf
p
fz
cept that boor him-self. Sounds like an im-po-
cept that boor him-self. Sounds like an im-po-
cept that boor him-self. I'll find the truth at length, I'll find the truth at length. Sounds like an im-po-si-tion.
pp

Scene V

Marie enters quickly followed by **Krushina** and **Ludmila**

Scene VI
Marie

Scene VIII
Kezal, Marie and Jenik

M. *risoluto* ... *più lento* ... Moderato.
Now just for spite, I re-fuse to sign, e'en were I sen-tenced to die for it!

J. Jenik *p dolce*
What re-

Moderato.

J. -ward is mine if I per-suade her to es-pouse our good friend Mi-cha's son?

Marie *f* ∧ ∧ *f*
M. How now? you would try your hand at per-

M. *con tutta la forza* ... *con dolore* ... (weeps bitterly) *
suad-ing me too? No, such dis-grace-ful ac-tions, nev - - er have been seen and nev-er heard!

Trio
Moderato assai. ♩=72.   Jenik *con sentimento*
J.
Be calm, dear, be calm, dear maid-en, tran-quil be,

J.
be calm, dear, and trust the words that I speak. Know you not, that hid-den here you may find glad-ness that you

173
L'istesso tempo, ma moderato.
Marie
Mar.
Now will I call the fam - i - lies,
and friends that are the dear - est
Jenik
J.
Now quick - ly fetch the fam - i - lies,
to wit - ness call those
Kezal
Kez.
fam - i - lies,
to wit - ness call those near - est
173
L'istesso tempo, ma moderato.
Fl. Ob.
Clar.
Fl. Ob.
Mar.
and all this tur - moil tor - ment - ing
and
J.
near - est
and all this stu - pid com - e - dy.
Kez.
and all this hes - i - ta - - - tion, dull,
and all this, all this, all this hes - i -
B'n.
Mar.
all this tur - moil tor - ment - ing
will fin - al - ly be end - - - - - - ed,
and all tor -
J.
and all this stu - pid com - - e - dy will
fin - al - ly be end - - - - ed,
and all this
Kez.
ta - tion, dull,
will fin - al - ly be end - - ed, will fin - al - ly be end ed, and all this

Scene IX

Finale.
Kezal, Marie, Jenik, Ludmila, Hata, Krushina, Micha, Kezal and Chorus

Allegro vivo. ♩.=104.

Scene X

OBSAH.